CLASSIC

HOWARD GOODALL'S

ENCHANTED CAROLS

SSA AND ORGAN (OR PIANO)

The full scores of the carols on the CD are available
as downloads from *fabermusicstore.com*

FABER *ff* MUSIC

This scoring is primarily intended for organ rather than piano, but I have largely left the registration to the organist to decide on according to the setting and choir. Some suggestions as to use of pedal have been included, with stems down in the left-hand stave. Pianists can play the accompaniments by making slight adaptations in places to avoid crossing hands.

Faber Music in association with Classic FM, a Global radio station.
Faber Music is the exclusive print publisher for all Global radio sheet music product.

© 2010 Faber Music Ltd
First published in 2010 by Faber Music Ltd
Bloomsbury House 74–77 Great Russell Street London WC1B 3DA
Music processed by Jeanne Roberts
Printed in England by Caligraving Ltd

ISBN10: 0-571-53561-5
EAN13: 978-0-571-53561-3

CONTENTS

ON THE ENCHANTED CAROLS

I am sure I am not alone in thinking of the twenty or so best-known Christmas carols as the perfect embodiment of the spirit and message of the festival, more so than all the other trappings of the season, adorable as they are – the trees, the baubles, the reindeer and that off-duty fireman/Rotary Club treasurer/lollipop attendant in his red coat and fluffy beard.

At the heart of the Nativity story lies an idea that can move Christians and non-Christians alike – namely that a child born in poverty and obscurity could change the world: this idea, under-pinned as it is with a plea for charity and human brotherhood, is expressed beautifully and memorably in those catchy, endearing tunes, many of them inherited from an aural, folk tradition that predates hymn books, candle processions and lavishly exhilarating organ accompaniments. When we think of our childhood experiences of Christmas, these melodies and ringing phrases are the trigger to the waves of emotion and memory attached to them – for many, indeed, carols *are* Christmas.

I feel as if I have had the arrangements of the most familiar of these carols somehow hard-wired into me, with their thrilling, last-verse descants and their reassuringly sonorous Anglican harmonies. So returning to the 'top twenty' list of carols for this collection presented me with a curious problem that as a composer I don't often have to confront: how to hear those tunes and words afresh, how to reinvent them for the soaring high voices of my *Enchanted Voices* group and how to give them 'my' sound without diluting their existing impact and charm.

I retain a deep respect for the arranging brilliance of David Willcocks and John Rutter who shaped the choral landscape of Christmas for the second half of the 20th century, but I had to put them out of my mind all the same, and here we are, anyway, in the 21st. Composing the brand new ones in the collection, mostly settings of medieval Latin words, was relatively easy by comparison with the task of rediscovering the blockbusters!

I had two guiding stars on this journey of reinvention – one was the distinctive vocal colour of the *Enchanted Voices* singers themselves (outstandingly skilled female choristers from the collegiate and cathedral 'evensong' tradition), interwoven with chamber organ, handbells and solo cello, a sound developed in the first *Enchanted Voices* CD with its settings of the *Beatitudes*. The success of that CD with the music-loving public made me think the combination of voices and its style (long, flowing phrases of newly-devised 'chant' against a contemplative, gently-undulating foundation) was one that worked well and could be used to good effect with carols old and new.

My other guiding star was the knowledge that the melodic arc of most classic carols is essentially derived from plainsong. Some of the best are plainsong in its purest form – *Veni, veni Emmanuel, Puer nobis nascitur, Guadete!* and so on. This seemed to chime (excuse the pun) with the musical canvas that was emerging not just from the *Enchanted Voices* CD but also as we took the group on tour around the country. Audiences were amazingly warm and appreciative of the *Enchanted Voices* troupe and I began to hear in my head how that ethereal, slightly other-worldly sound might adapt itself to the plainsong sources of the carols. The fit felt right.

In fact, as is surprisingly common with Christmas music, I composed the settings in this collection in the baking heat of a French summer, so I was obliged to let my imagination take complete control of my writing about the snow, the figgy pudding and those freezing, un-tented shepherds! As with all my composing, though, the music emerges, fully formed, out of nothing, seemingly, and very soon I was immersed in those hauntingly high soprano lines, gliding effortlessly above the horizon, echoing across the centuries, somehow bringing together the ancient purity of the medieval past and the here and now. I hope we have succeeded in making the meeting between them as rewarding to listen to and to perform as it has been to conceive.

Howard Goodall

THE FIRST NOWELL

Anon.
arr. Howard Goodall

ANGELS, FROM THE REALMS OF GLORY

James Montgomery

Traditional French
arr. Howard Goodall

SOLO
An - gels, from the _ realms of glo - ry, wing your flight o'er _ all the earth;

ye who sang cre - a - tion's sto - ry, now pro - claim Mes - si - ah's birth.

De - o. Glo - - - - - - - - - ri - a

De - o. Glo - - - - - - - - - ri - a

De - o. Glo - - - - - - - - - ri - a

in ex - cel - sis De - - o.

in ex - cel - sis De - - o.

in ex - cel - sis De - - o.

SOLO

Sa - ges, leave your con - tem - pla - tions, bright - er vi - sions

O LITTLE TOWN OF BETHLEHEM

Phillips Brooks

Forest Green
arr. Howard Goodall

17 hopes and fears of all the years are met in thee to-night.

21 *mp* Oh morn-ing stars, to-ge - ther pro-claim the ho-ly

25 birth, and prais-es sing to God the king and peace to men on

29 earth; For Christ is born of Ma - ry; and, ga-thered all a -

33 -bove, while mor-tals sleep, the an-gels keep their watch of won-d'ring

37
love.

pp

How si - lent - ly, how si - lent - ly, the

41
won - drous gift is giv'n! So God im - parts to hu - man hearts the

45
bless - ings of his heav'n. No_ ear may hear his_ com - ing; but

49
in this world of sin, where meek souls will re - ceive him still, the

53
dear Christ en - ters in.

mf

Oh ho - ly Child of

Beth - le - hem, des - cend to_ us, we pray; Cast out our sin and

en - ter_ in: be born in_ us to - day. We_ hear the Christ-mas

an - gels the great glad tid - ings tell: O come to us, a -

- bide with us, our Lord Em - ma - nu - el!

- bide with us, our Lord Em - ma - nu - el!

poco rit.

GAUDETE!

Piae Cantiones 1582

Anon.
arr. Howard Goodall

IN DULCI JUBILO

Traditional
arr. Howard Goodall

THE ANGEL GABRIEL

Sabine Baring-Gould

Traditional Basque Carol
arr. Howard Goodall

40

Christ, was born,___ In Beth-le-hem, all on a Christ-mas morn;___ And

Chris-tian folk through-out the world will ev-er say:___ Most high-ly fa-vour'd la-dy,

Glo-___ri-a!___

Più largo
ALL
Glo-___ri-a!

SUSSEX CAROL

Traditional
arr. Howard Goodall

Lyrics:
News of great joy, news of great mirth, News of our merciful King's birth.

Then why should men on earth be so sad Since our Redeemer made us glad? Then why should men on earth be so sad Since our Redeemer made us glad?

44

VENI, VENI, EMMANUEL

Traditional
arr. Howard Goodall

SILENT NIGHT

Josef Mohr

Franz Gruber
arr. Howard Goodall

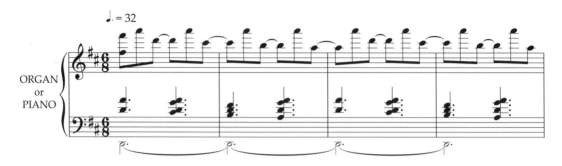

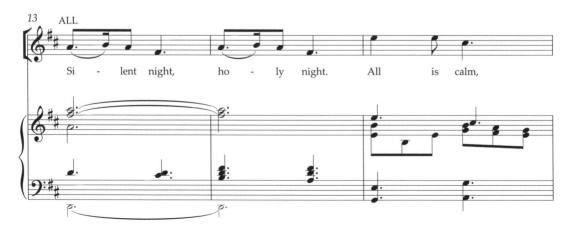

Si - lent night, ho - ly night. All is calm,

STELLA QUAM VIDERANT MAGI

THE WISE MEN AND THE STAR

Howard Goodall

e - rat. Stel - la quam vi - de-rant Ma -

- gi ab O - ri - en-te, an-te-ce-de-bat e - os, do -

nec ve - ni - rent ad lo - cum u - bi pu - er e - rat, u -

bi pu - er e - rat.

60

ANGELUS AD VIRGINEM

THE ANGEL SECRETLY VISITS THE VIRGIN

Howard Goodall

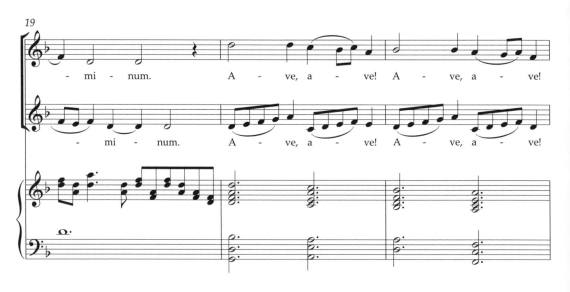

SOLO 1: post ex-i-it, et in - i-it con-flic-tum af - fi - gens hu - me - ro;___

SOLO 2: post ex - i - it, et in - i-it con-flic-tum af - fi - gens hu - me - ro;___

___ Cru - cem qua de - dit ic - tum hos - ti mor - ti -

___ Cru - cem__ qua de - dit ic - tum hos - ti mor -

- fe - ro. A - ve, a - ve! A - ve, a - ve!

S. 1 ALL

-ti - fe - ro. A - ve, a - ve! A - ve, a - ve!

S. 2 ALL

A SOLIS ORTUS CARDINE

FROM LANDS THAT SEE THE SUN ARISE

Coelius Sedulius   Howard Goodall

VERBUM CARO FACTUM EST

THE WORD WAS MADE FLESH

Text based on John 1: 14

Howard Goodall

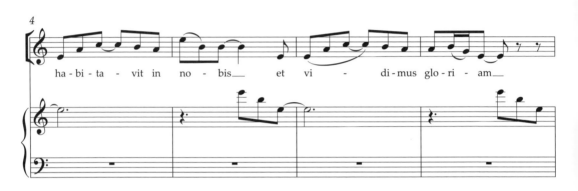

62

_a Pa - tre ple - num gra-ti - ae___ et___ ve - ri -_

66

_- ta - - tis.___ Al - le - lu - ia,___

70

_al - le - lu - ia,___ al - le - lu - ia,___

74

_al - le - lu - - ia,___ al - le -_

LULLABY OF WINTER

Words and Music by
Howard Goodall

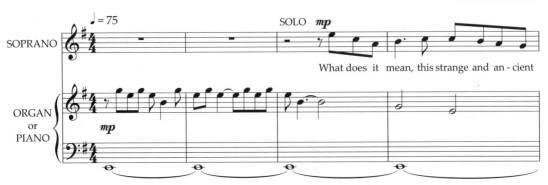

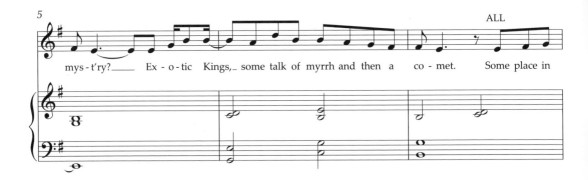

had one God, and He was on their side. What do they mean, these ref-'ren-ces to pro-phets? They seem to re-in-force the claim that it's a fic-tion. Two wan-d'ring Jews they were___ with no place to rest, A stink-ing cave would have to do, and stuff their pride. No doubt they loved him,___ the ti-ny

26

bairn___ (the sleep-ing rough and be-ing des-ti-tute a - side).

29

What does it mean, that i-con of the Vir-gin?___ It fights with

32

na-ture, makes re-li-gion look_ un-know-ing.

ALL *div.*
warmer

Oh,___ but still it

35

e - choes — We know the de-tails creak, but does that mat-ter? And

mf

oh,_____ it would be ea - sy_____ to mock it till the stained - glass vi - sions

shat - ter. Yet there in Pa - les - tine,_____ in that de - sert chill,_____ we are re -

- mind - ed of some truths that do not wane: God lives in - side us,_____ runs through our

blood, Birth is ex - pe - ri - ence both sa - cred and hu - mane.

Oh,_____ but still it e - choes,_____ We know the de - tails creak, but does that mat - ter? And oh,_____ it would be ea - sy_____ to mock it till the stained - glass vi - sions shat - ter, Yet there in Pa - les - tine,_____ in that de - sert chill,_____ we are re - mind - ed of some truths that do not wane:

SOLO

That for each home - less girl like her there are two end - ings: one where we

A LITTLE CHILD THERE IS YBORN

Anon.

Howard Goodall

26 (ALL)
It___ fell up - on the high mid - night, Shone the stars both

30
fair and bright,___ the an - gels sang with___ all their might:

34
Glo - ri - a Ti - bi, Do - mi - ne,___ Qui na - tus es de___ vir - gi - ne.

39 SOLO
Three Kings there came with their pres - ents, Myrrh and gold and

43
frank - in - cense,___ As clerk - ës sing in___ their se - quence:

WE WISH YOU A MERRY CHRISTMAS

Traditional
arr. Howard Goodall

PUER NOBIS NASCITUR

UNTO US IS BORN A SON

Piae Cantiones 1582

Anon.
arr. Howard Goodall

Duc nos, tu - a gra - ti - a Ad gau - di - a su - per - na, ad gau - di - a su - per - na.

Duc nos, tu - a gra - ti - a Ad gau - di - a su - per - na, ad gau - di - a su - per - na.

Ca - nant lae - ti Do - mi - no glo - ri - a in ex - cel - sis, Ho - mi - ni cor - de bo - no, pax et

Ca - nant lae - ti Do - mi - no glo - ri - a in ex - cel - sis, Ho - mi - ni cor - de bo - no, pax et

sa - lus in ter - ris, et sa - lus in ter - ris.

sa - lus in ter - ris, et sa - lus in ter - ris.

CHORAL SIGNATURE SERIES

Thomas Adès	The Fayrfax Carol
	January Writ
Julian Anderson	Four American Choruses
Brendan Ashe	For the Fallen
	Sanctus
David Bednall	Hail, Gladdening Light
	If Ye Love Me
	O Praise God in His Holiness
	The Souls of the Righteous
Jonathan Dove	Ecce Beatam Lucem
	Into Thy Hands
	Seek Him that Maketh the Seven Stars
	Wellcome, all Wonders in One Sight!
	Who Killed Cock Robin?
Vladimír Godár	Dormi, Jesu
	Regina Coeli
Howard Goodall	In Memoriam Anne Frank
	Jubilate Deo
	Lead, Kindly Light
	The Lord is My Shepherd
	Love Divine
	The Marlborough Canticles
	Spared
Francis Grier	Alleluia! I Bring You News of Great Joy
	Two Advent Responsories
Jonathan Harvey	Come, Holy Ghost
	Remember, O Lord
Malcolm Hayes	Corpus Christi
Nigel Hess	Jubilate Deo
Matthew Hindson	Home
Morten Lauridsen	Ave Dulcissima Maria
	Ave Maria
	O Come, Let Us Sing Unto The Lord
	O Magnum Mysterium
	O Nata Lux
	Ubi Caritas et Amor
Alexander L'Estrange	Lute-book Lullaby
	On Eagles' Wings
	Prayers for Peace
Wayne Marshall	Magnificat & Nunc Dimittis in C
Matthew Martin	Adam Lay Ybounden
	Ecce Concipies
Colin Matthews	The Angels' Carol
Nicholas Maw	One Foot in Eden Still, I Stand
Margaret Rizza	Ave Maria
	Mary Slept
	O Sapientia
	Veni Jesu
Peter Sculthorpe	Morning Song for the Christ Child
John Woolrich	Spring in Winter

To buy Faber Music publications or to find out about the full range of titles available
please contact your local music retailer or Faber Music sales enquiries:

Faber Music Ltd, Burnt Mill, Elizabeth Way, Harlow CM20 2HX
Tel: +44 (0) 1279 82 89 82   Fax: +44 (0) 1279 82 89 83
sales@fabermusic.com   fabermusic.com   expressprintmusic.com